STYLE WORKOUT

for solo saxophone

Studies in classical, jazz, rock and latin styles

JAMES RAE

UE 21 232
ISMN: M-008-07506-3
UPC 8-03452-02116-2
ISBN 3-7024-2569-1

9.95

Contents
Inhalt • Table des Matières

Classical

Jazz (Swing) 18

Rock

Latin

Preface

This collection of forty original studies will familiarize players from elementary through to intermediate standard with the various types of music commonly encountered in the solo and band repertoire of today. The studies are short to moderate in length and are grouped into four sections: ***Classical, Jazz, Rock*** and ***Latin***. They are all written in player-friendly keys in order to maximize concentration on stylistic interpretation. Each study deals with a particular aspect of style and also has a brief descriptive sentence to help the student.

As a complete musician, it is important to be conversant with all styles of music and be able to deliver the correct interpretation whenever necessary. Many players are *pigeonholed* into one category or another because they are only versed in one particular genre and tend to play everything in the same style. This is often true of instrumentalists who are essentially classically trained when required to play jazz phrasing. The studies in this book are designed to encourage and prompt the student into adopting the correct *feel* for each style.

Feel in music can be defined as the ability of the performer to communicate the thoughts of the composer to the audience in the *correct* musical *dialect*. A good sense of feel can be acquired not only by regular practice, but also by listening to all types of music. Listening is the most effective way of absorbing any musical style.

Classical, Jazz, Rock and Latin Styles

Music played stylistically correctly, often sounds different from how it appears on the page. This is particularly the case with jazz due to the use of *swing phrasing* which affects the values of notes and rests. In the case of classical, rock and latin styles the music is basically played as written although there are more subtle differences in the interpretation. This is mainly evident in the *weight* of the accented notes. Accents are generally played more strongly in rock and latin styles than those in classical music. Although latin music is rhythmically strong, it has to also maintain a *laid back* feel. Rock music, on the other hand, requires a far more *solid* approach.

Comparing various styles in music can be likened to the comparison of English spoken in various parts of the British Isles, Australasia or North America. It is essentially the same language but sounds quite different because of the dialect or accent. These differences cannot easily be described in words but can only be mastered by perceptive listening and imitation. The same principle applies to all styles of music.

For further repertoire in Classical, Jazz, Rock and Latin styles at the level of this book see the opposite page. The Listening List provides a few titles to help bring you closer to these musical styles.

Repertoire List

Classical
Easy Classical Studies (UE 17770)
Classical Album (UE 17772)

Jazz and Rock
Jazz Zone (UE 21030)
Easy Studies in Jazz and Rock (UE 19392)
Easy Jazzy Saxophone (UE 16578)
Easy Jazzy Saxophone Duets (UE 16551)
Jazzy Saxophone 1 (UE 18827)
Jazzy Saxophone 2 (UE 19362)
Jazzy Saxophone Duets (UE 19395)
Blue Saxophone (UE 19765)
Blue Duets for Saxophones (UE 14051)
Play-Along Saxophone (UE 31854)

Latin
Latin Saxophone (UE 17364)
Latin Duets for Saxophones (UE 21074)
Play-Along Saxophone – Latin (UE 32375)

All styles
Play it Cool (UE 21100)
Take Ten (UE 18836)
Take Another Ten (UE 21170)

Listening List

Classical
Mussorgsky / Ravel: *The Old Castle* from *Pictures at an exhibition*
Bizet: *Intermezzo* from *L'Arlesienne Suite No. 2*
Prokofiev: *Troika* from *Lieutenant Kije*

Jazz Albums
Count Basie: *The Atomic Mr. Basie*
Miles Davis: *Kind of Blue*
Oscar Peterson: *Night Train*

Jazz / Rock / Fusion Albums
Weather Report: *Heavy Weather*
Brecker Brothers: *Out of the Loop*
Herbie Hancock: *Headhunters*

Latin Albums
Maraca: *Descarga Total*
Stan Getz / Astrud Gilberto
Francis Albert Sinatra and Antonio Carlos Jobim

Vorwort

Mit dieser Sammlung von vierzig speziell für diese Ausgabe komponierten Übungsstücken lernen die Schüler von der Grund- bis zur Mittelstufe verschiedene Musikstile kennen, die im heutigen Solo- und Ensemblerepertoire gewöhnlich vorkommen. Die Länge der Stücke ist kurz bis mittel und sie wurden in vier Gruppen eingeteilt: ***Klassik***, ***Jazz***, ***Rock*** und ***Latin***. Alle Stücke stehen in *einfachen* Tonarten, um die Aufmerksamkeit auf die stilistische Gestaltung zu konzentrieren. Jedes Stück beschäftigt sich mit einem besonderen Aspekt eines Stils und enthält einen kurzen beschreibenden Satz, um dem Schüler zu helfen.

Jeder Musiker sollte danach streben, mit allen Stilrichtungen vertraut zu sein, um die richtige Interpretation zum erforderlichen Zeitpunkt anbieten zu können. Viele Spieler werden in die eine oder andere Schublade gesteckt, weil sie nur mit einem bestimmten Genre vertraut sind und alles andere im gleichen Stil spielen. Das gilt besonders für Musiker mit einer grundsätzlich klassischen Ausbildung, wenn sie im Jazzstil spielen sollen. Die Stücke in diesem Buch wurden geschrieben, um den Schüler zu ermutigen, sich das richtige *Feeling* für jeden Stil anzueignen.

Feeling in der Musik kann als die Fähigkeit des Interpreten definiert werden, dem Publikum die Gedanken des Komponisten in der *richtigen musikalischen Sprache* zu vermitteln. Ein gutes Feeling bekommt man nicht nur durch regelmäßiges Üben, sondern auch durch das Anhören verschiedener Musikarten. Zuhören ist die wirksamste Form, einen Musikstil aufzunehmen.

Klassische, Jazz-, Rock- und lateinamerikanische Stile

Stilistisch richtig gespielte Musik klingt oft anders als sie notiert ist. Das gilt besonders für den Jazz wegen der *swingenden Phrasierung,* wodurch sich Notenwerte und Pausen ändern. Die klassische, Rock- und lateinamerikanische Musik wird grundsätzlich wie notiert gespielt, dort gibt es allerdings subtilere Nuancen in der Interpretation. Dies wird hauptsächlich in der *Gewichtung* der akzentuierten Noten deutlich. Akzente werden in Rock- und lateinamerikanischen Stilen stärker hervorgehoben als in der klassischen Musik. Lateinamerikanische Musik ist zwar sehr rhythmusbetont, aber man sollte auch ein *Laid Back Feeling* bewahren. Rockmusik dagegen erfordert einen sehr viel kräftigeren Zugang.

Der Vergleich zwischen verschiedenen Musikstilen ist dem Vergleich zwischen den verschiedenen Ausprägungen der englischen Sprache in den diversen Teilen Großbritanniens, des australisch-asiatischen Raums oder Nordamerikas nicht unähnlich. Eigentlich ist es die gleiche Sprache, aber sie klingt aufgrund des Dialekts oder Akzents jeweils ganz anders. Diese Unterschiede können nicht leicht mit Worten beschrieben, sondern nur durch aufmerksames Hören und Nachahmen gemeistert werden. Das gleiche Prinzip gilt auch für die verschiedenen Musikstile.

Auf Seite 5 findest du eine Repertoireliste von klassischer, Jazz-, Rock- und lateinamerikanischer Musik im Schwierigkeitsgrad dieses Heftes. Außerdem gibt es einige Anregungen für Hörbeispiele, die dir die in diesem Heft beschriebenen Musikstile näher bringen.

Préface

Ce recueil de quarante études originales familiarisera les pianistes du degré élémentaire au degré intermédiaire avec les types variés de musique communément rencontrées dans le répertoire soliste et d'ensemble d'aujourd'hui. Les études sont d'une longueur courte à modérée et sont groupées en quatre sections : ***Classique, Jazz, Rock*** et ***Latino***. Elles sont toutes écrites dans des tonalités aisément abordables, de manière à maximaliser la concentration sur l'interprétation stylistique. Chaque étude traite d'un aspect stylistique particulier et dispose d'une brève phrase descriptive destinée à aider l'étudiant.

Un musicien complet devrait connaître tous les styles musicaux et être capable de prodiguer l'interprétation correcte quand cela est nécessaire. De nombreux pianistes sont « logés » dans l'une ou l'autre catégorie car ils sont seulement versés dans un genre particulier et inclinent à tout jouer dans le même style. Ceci est souvent le cas d'instrumentistes qui ont une formation essentiellement classique alors qu'il est requis de jouer dans un phrasé jazz. Les études de ce recueil sont conçues pour encourager et inciter l'étudiant à adopter le *toucher* correct pour chaque style.

Le *toucher* en musique peut être défini par l'aptitude de l'exécutant à communiquer les pensées du compositeur au public dans le *dialecte* musical *correct*. Un bon sens du toucher peut être acquis non seulement par la pratique régulière mais aussi par l'écoute de tous les types musicaux. L'écoute est le moyen le plus efficace d'absorber tout style musical.

Styles classique, jazz, rock et latino

La musique jouée correctement d'un point de vue stylistique sonne souvent d'une manière différente suivant la manière dont elle apparaît sur la page. C'est particulièrement le cas avec le jazz, suite à l'usage du *phrasé swing* qui affecte les valeurs des notes et des silences. Dans le cas des styles classique, rock et latino, la musique est essentiellement jouée telle qu'elle est écrite, bien qu'il y ait des différences plus subtiles dans l'interprétation. C'est surtout évident dans le *poids* des notes accentuées. Les accents sont généralement joués plus énergiquement dans les styles rock et latino que dans le style classique. Bien que la musique latino soit rythmiquement forte, elle doit aussi maintenir un sentiment de *suspens*. La musique rock requiert par contre une approche bien plus *solide*.

La comparaison des styles variés en musique peut être comparée à l'anglais parlé dans différentes parties des îles britanniques, d'Australie ou d'Amérique du Nord. Il s'agit essentiellement de la même langue mais elle sonne complètement différemment en raison du dialecte ou de l'accent. Ces différences ne peuvent être facilement décrites par des mots mais peuvent être seulement maîtrisées par l'écoute perceptive et l'imitation. Le même principe s'applique à tous les styles de musique.

Pour un plus large répertoire dans les styles classique, jazz, rock et latino correspondant à ce niveau, voir page 5.

Classical

1. Proclamation

Bekanntmachung • Proclamation

► Play this piece firmly with a strong sense of pulse.
Spiele dieses Stück entschlossen und fühle den Puls sehr stark.
Joue cette pièce avec fermeté avec un sens solide de la pulsation.

2. The First Waltz

Erster Walzer • La première valse

► Aim for smooth playing here and don't rush the quavers.
Bemühe dich hier um ein fließendes Spiel und lasse die Achtelnoten nicht davonlaufen.
Vise ici un jeu régulier et n'accélère pas les croches.

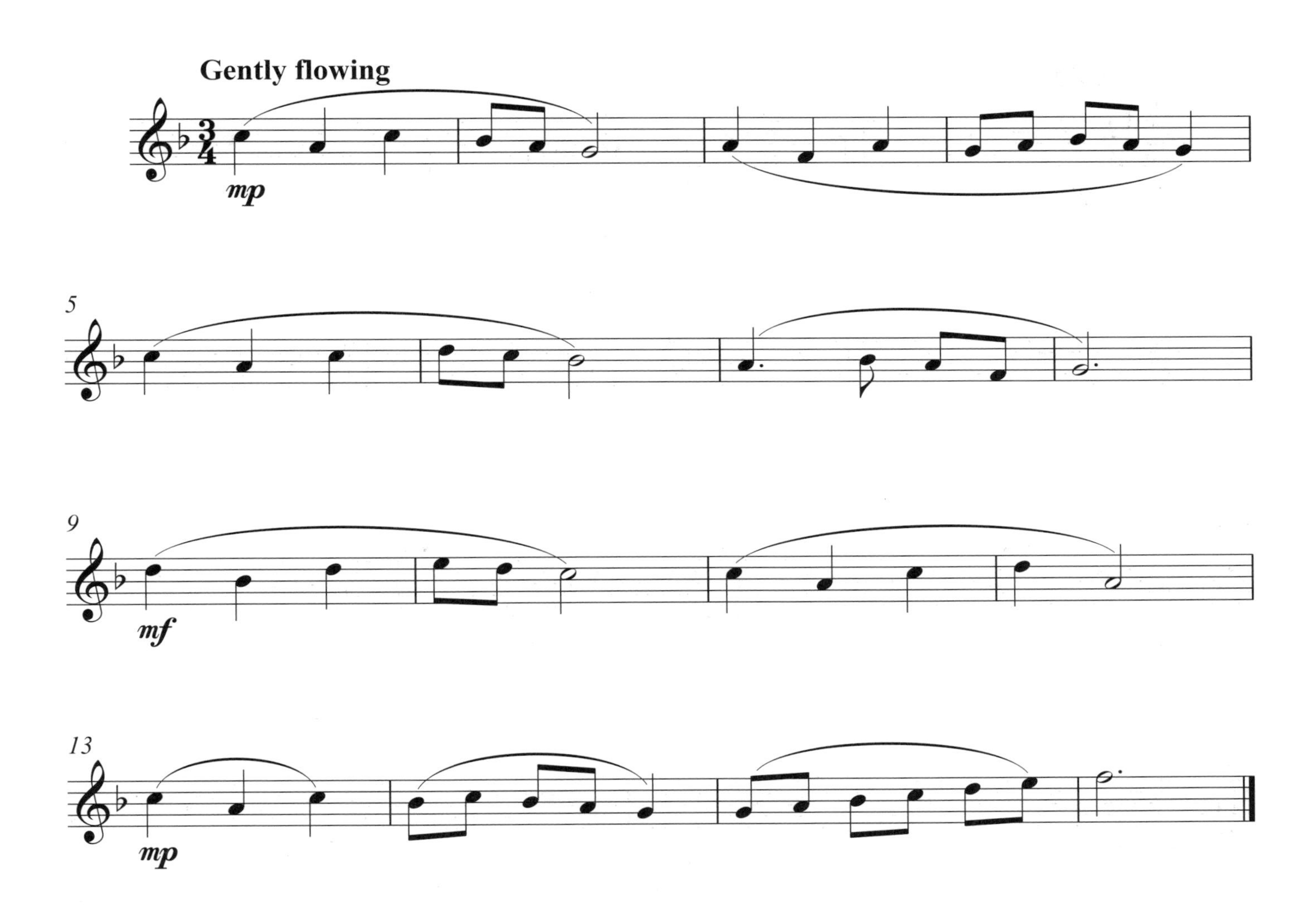

3. Little Prelude

Kleines Präludium • Petit prélude

► Make sure that all intervals are played cleanly with no *spare notes* in between.
Pass auf, dass alle Intervalle sauber, d. h. ohne überzählige Töne *gespielt werden.*
Assure-toi que tous les intervalles soient joués de manière propre sans *notes inutiles* intermédiaires.

4. Autumn Clouds

Herbstwolken • Nuages d'automne

► Take nice deep breaths in order to support the long phrases and observe all dynamics.

Hole ein paar Mal tief Luft um die Spannung der langen Phrasen durchzuhalten und befolge alle Vortragsanweisungen bezüglich der Dynamik.

Respire largement, afin de soutenir les longues phrases et observe toutes les nuances.

Classical

5. Jig in D

Gigue in D • Gigue en ré

► Play this with a sense of *lilt* and keep a strong *2 in a bar feel* throughout.

Spiele dieses Stück im wiegenden 6/8tel-Takt und betone durchgehend die zwei schweren Zählzeiten jedes Taktes.

Joue ceci avec un sentiment d'élévation et garde d'un bout à l'autre une sensation de mesure à 2.

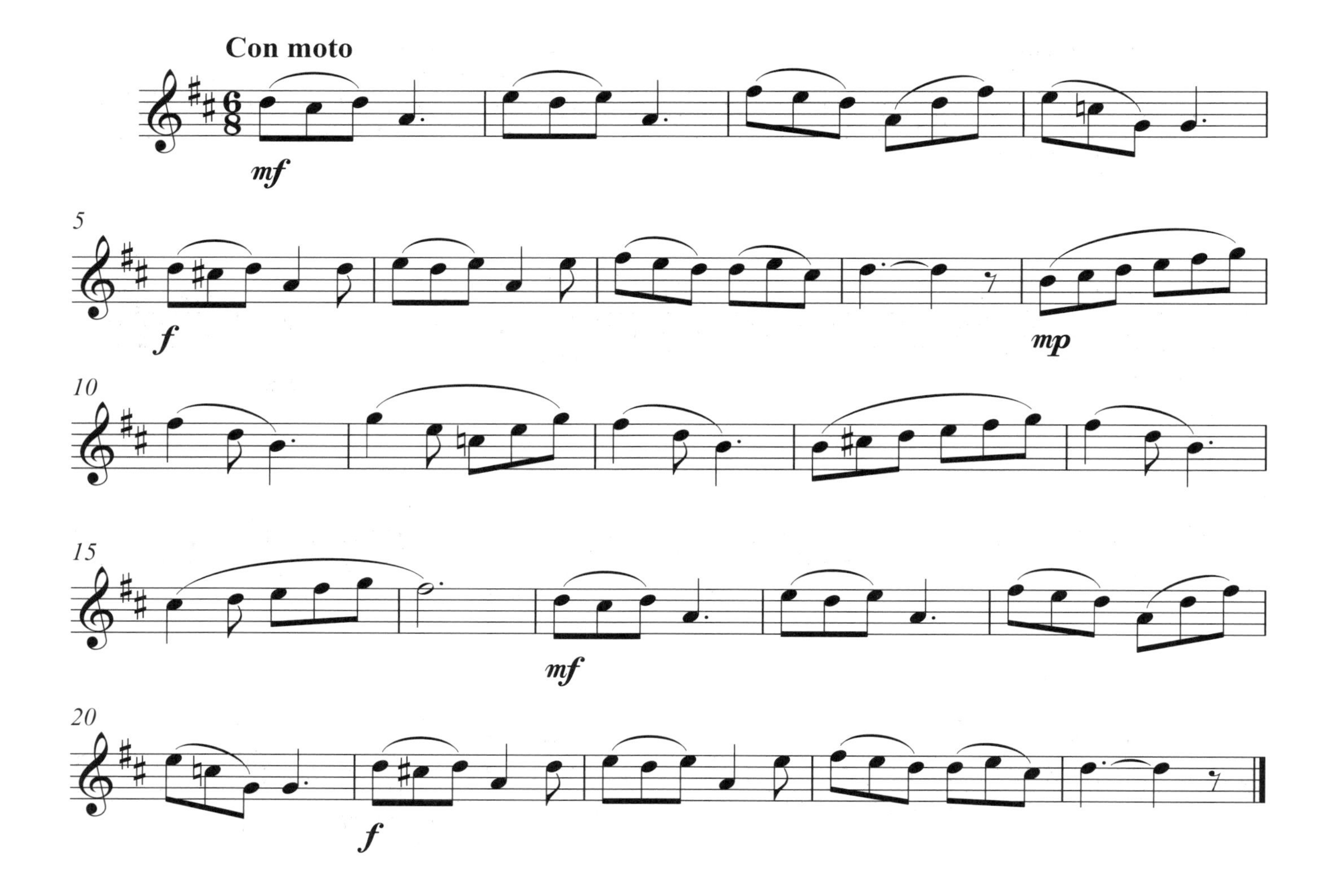

6. Open Spaces

Weite Räume • Espaces ouverts

Classical

► Use a firm finger action in order to play the intervals evenly.

Bewege deine Finger sehr entschlossen, um die Intervalle gleichmäßig zu spielen.

Emploie une ferme action du doigt de manière à jouer les intervalles avec égalité.

Classical

7. Chandelier Waltz

Kronleuchter-Walzer • Valse du lustre

► Play this piece with a great deal of energy and expression.
Spiele dieses Stück mit sehr viel Energie und Ausdruck.
Joue cette pièce avec beaucoup d'énergie et d'expression.

Classical

8. Strange, But True

Komisch, aber wahr • Etrange mais vrai

► Play this with great flexibility and always aim to shape the phrases well.

Spiele dieses Stück mit großer Beweglichkeit und bemühe dich immer, die musikalischen Phrasen zu gestalten.

Joue avec une grande flexibilité et vise toujours à bien façonner les phrases.

9. Scale Model

Tonleiter-Modell • Modèle de gamme

► Always aim to play the semi-quavers as evenly as possible and try not to rush.
Bemühe dich immer, die Sechszehntelnoten so gleichmäßig wie möglich zu spielen und lasse das Tempo nicht davonlaufen.
Vise toujours à jouer les doubles croches aussi égales que possible et essaie de ne pas accélérer.

10. Epilogue

Nachwort • Epilogue

► Play this piece with much expression, but never lose track of the pulse.
Spiele dieses Stück mit viel Ausdruck, verliere dabei aber nie das Gefühl für den Puls.
Joue cette pièce avec beaucoup d'expression, mais ne perds jamais la trajectoire de la pulsation.

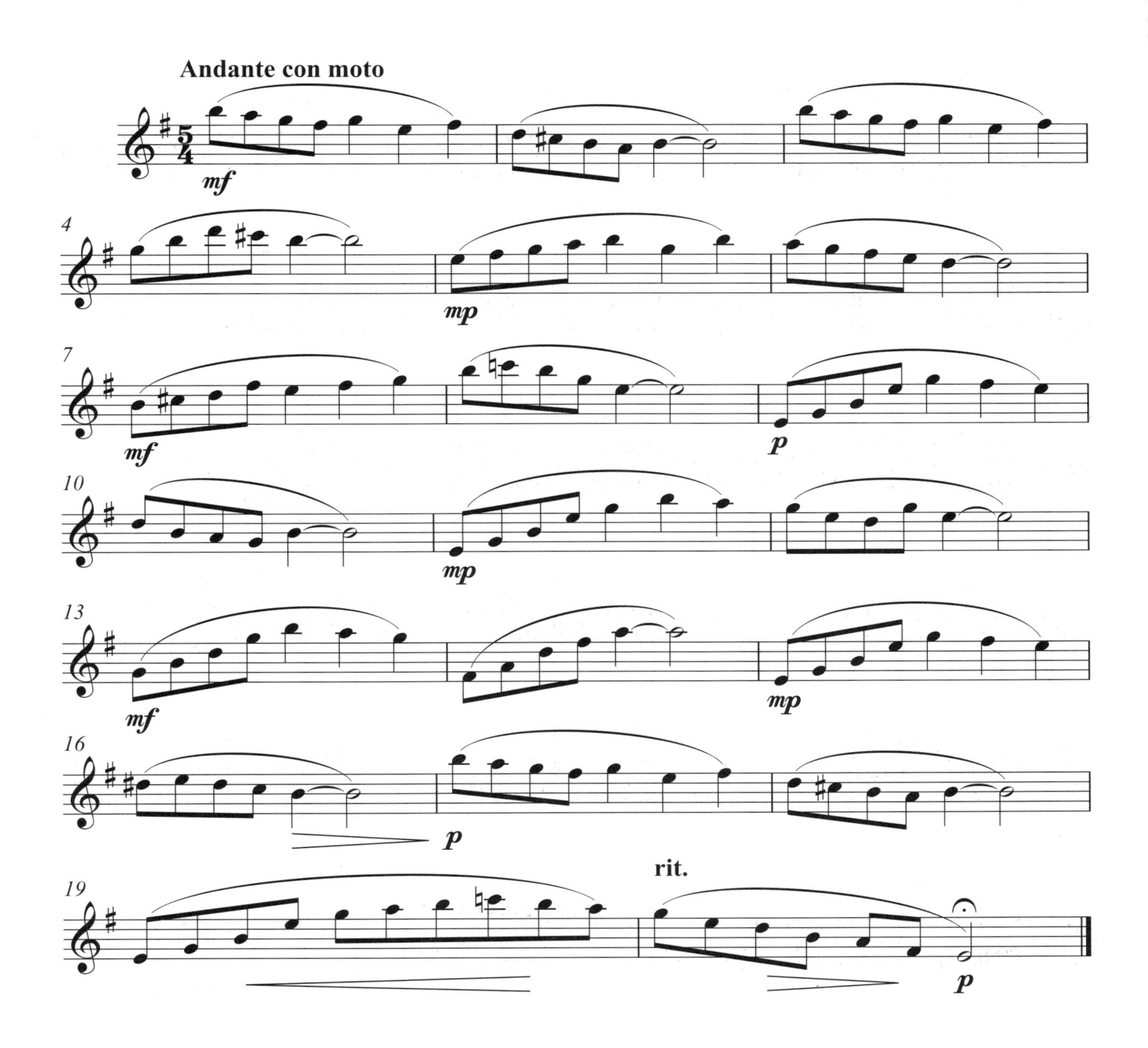

Jazz (Swing)

All quavers in this section of the book are to be swung.
Alle Achtelnoten in diesem Abschnitt des Buches sollen swingend gespielt werden.
Toutes les croches de cette section du recueil doivent être oscillantes.

Swing Quavers

In a lot of Jazz music, the quavers are often said to be *swung*. This means that the first of every pair of quavers on the beat is twice as long as the second (tripletised). Sometimes they are written as *straight* quavers ♫ and sometimes as a dotted quaver followed by a semi-quaver ♪.♬, but there will always be an indication of the style from the tempo marking, e.g. *Swing feel*. Many composers now use the symbol ♫ = ♩♪ (3) to denote that all quavers in the music should be swung.

N.B. This also applies to quaver rests.

e.g. **With a Swing** (♫ = ♩♪ (3))

Swingende Achtelnoten

Im Jazz sollen die Achtelnoten häufig *swingend* gespielt werden. Das heißt, dass die erste von zwei Achtelnoten pro Zählzeit doppelt so lang ist wie die zweite (triolisch). Manchmal werden sie wie *normale* Achtelnoten ♫ und manchmal punktiert ♪.♬ notiert, aber es gibt immer eine Anmerkung des Stils bei der Tempobezeichnung, z. B. *Swing feel*. Viele Komponisten verwenden heutzutage auch das Symbol ♫ = ♩♪ (3), um darauf hinzuweisen, dass alle Achtelnoten in der Musik swingend gespielt werden sollen.

Übrigens: Das trifft auch auf Achtelpausen zu.

z.B. **With a Swing** (♫ = ♩♪ (3))

Croches oscillantes

Dans de nombreuses musiques de jazz, les croches sont souvent qualifiées d'« oscillantes » : ceci signifie que la première de chaque paire sur le temps est deux fois plus longue que la seconde (triplée). Quelquefois elles sont écrites comme des noires « régulières » ♫ et quelquefois comme croche pointée/doubles croches ♪.♬. Mais il y aura toujours une indication du style à partir de l'indication de tempo, par example *Swing feel*. Aujourd'hui de nombreux compositeurs utilisent le symbole ♫ = ♩♪ (3) pour signifier que toutes les croches de la musique devraient être oscillantes.

N.B. Ceci s'applique aussi aux demi soupirs.

p.ex. **With a Swing** (♫ = ♩♪ (3))

HAWK GETS BIRD

GORDON LEWIN

★ ♪ —start note slightly flat and lip up to true pitch

11. That'll Do Nicely!

Das reicht allemal! • Je le ferai bien !

► Keep a cool head with this one and don't be tempted to rush.
Behalte in diesem Stück einen klaren Kopf und lasse das Tempo nicht davonlaufen.
Garde la tête froide et ne sois pas tenté d'accélérer.

Jazz

12. Nobody's Blues

► Use *legato tonguing* (doo doo doo doo etc.) to achieve the correct blues feel in this piece.

Verwende einen gebundenen Zungenstoß *(duh duh duh duh usw.), um in diesem Stück das richtige Bluesgefühl zu bekommen.*

Utilise la *langue legato* (doo doo doo doo, etc.) pour achever la sensation correcte de blues de cette pièce.

Fig.150. *Fred Gillford's photograph of his own Clayton & Shuttleworth wagon (No.48425) in his yard at Daybrook, Notts.*

Fig.151. *In the mid-thirties the yard of Baldwin Bros. at Wadhurst, Sussex, was like a working museum. John Russell found Aveling & Porter No.1232, a three shafter, with Watt-type governors and cast iron rims to the wheels.*

Fig.152. *Bennett's Super Sentinel (No.6253), converted to a tractor, in Commercial Road, Liverpool, September 23, 1950.* [Charles Lloyd]

Bibliography

The source material for this book is mainly in the possession of the Road Locomotive Society or of its individual members, principally in the files of its Journal, the Portfolio scheme, the owners' lists and Alan Duke's makers' lists. This was supplemented, in the cases of the chapters dealing with fairground matters and timber hauling, by personal communications from friends engaged, past or present, in the respective trades, and from private documents in their possession. Other sources include the following magazines:

The Engineer
Commercial Motor
La Vie Automobile
Steaming
Implement & Machinery Review
Motor Traction
Die Reform
Journal of the Institution of Mechanical Engineers

,and the books listed below:

Author	Title	Place	Publisher	Year
Andreas Kuntz	*Der Dampfpflug*	Marburg	Jonas	1979
F.M.L.Thomson (Ed)	*Horses in European Economic History*	Reading	Brit.Agric.Hist.Soc	1983
G.Soper	*Modern Methods of Street Cleaning*	London	Constable	1909
-----	*Roads & Road Construction Yearbook*	London	Carriers Publishing	Various
T.Sherwen	*The Bomford Story*	Evesham	Bomford&Evershed	1978
C.Dunbar	*The Rise of Road Transport 1919-1939*	Shepperton	Ian Allan	1981
W.J.Gordon	*The Horse World of London* (reprint)	Newton Abbott	David&Charles	1971
----	*Annual Reports, National Traction Engine &Users Association.*	London		various
H.Winkel and K.Herrmann	*Development of Agricultural Technology} in the 19th + 20th Centuries*	Ostfildern	ScripturaMercaturae	1984
B.Newman	*One Hundred Years of Good Company*	Lincoln	Ruston&Hornsby	1957
A.Glen	*The Highway,Locomotive&Turnpike Acts*	London	Knight	1879
M.F.Robiou de la Tréhonnais	*Revue Agricole de l'Angleterre*	Paris	Firmin Didot	1859
A.Gordon	*A Treatise upon Elemental Locomotion*	London	Tegg	1836
C.Bryner Jones (Ed)	*Livestock of the Farm*	London	Gresham	1919
Lord Montague of Beaulieu and A.Bird	*Steam Cars 1770 - 1970*	London	Cassell	1971
L.T.C.Rolt	*The Cornish Giant*	London	Lutterworth Press	1960
	Waterloo Ironworks	Newton Abbott	David&Charles	1969
W.W.Dickinson and A.Titley	*Richard Trevithick, the Engineer and the Man*	Cambridge	Cambridge University Press	1934
C.F.T.Young	*The Economy of Steam Power on Common Roads*	London	Atchley	1860
W.Fletcher	*Steam Locomotion on Common Roads*	London	Spon	1891
	English & American Steam Carriages and Traction Engines	London	Spon	1901
W.Norris	*Modern Steam Road Wagons 1906*	London	Longmans Green	1906
W.Plowden	*The Motor Car & Politics in Britain 1896 - 1970*	London	Bodley Head	1971
R.E.B.Crompton	*Reminiscences*	London	Constable	1928
T.R.Nicholson	*The Birth of the British Motor Car* (3vols)	London	MacMillan	1982
D.Braithwaite	*Fairground Architecture*	London	Evelyn	1968
	Savage of Kings Lynn	Cambridge	Stephens	1975
R.W.Kidner	*The Steam Lorry*	Lingfield	Oakwood Press	1948
A.Fay	*Some Bioscope Shows & their Engines*	Lingfield	Oakwood Press	1966
Encyclopædia Britannica 9th + 10th Editions		London+Edinburgh	A.& C.Black	

References to works by R.L.S. members.

As these works are so well-known only the authors' names and the short titles are given. An asterisk by the author's name denotes a past-President.

Author	Short title
*R.H.Clark	*Steam Engine Builders of Suffolk, Essex and Cambridgeshire*
	Steam Engine Builders of Norfolk
	Steam Engine Builders of Lincolnshire
	Chronicles of a Country Works
	Development of the English Traction Engine
	Development of the English Steam Wagon
	Traction Engine Miscellany
*T.W.B.Ellis + A.E.Olive	*100 Years of Road Rollers*
F.H.Gillford	*The Traction Engine*
D.R.Grace + D.Phillips	*Ransomes of Ipswich*
*J.Haining + C.Tyler	*Ploughing by Steam*
*W.J.Hughes	*Century of Traction Engines*
M.A.Kelly	*Overtype Steam Road Wagon*
	Undertype Steam Road Wagon
*E.E.Kimbell	*Compleat Traction Engineman*
M.R.Lane	*Pride of the Road*
	Story of the Steam Plough Works
	Burrell Showmen's Engines
*T.McTaggart	*Pioneers of Heavy Haulage*
	The Big Box
*T.B.Paisley	*Fowells of St.Ives*
J.L.Thomas	*The Sentinel*
C.Tyler	*Digging by Steam*

13. Stake-Out

Überwachung • Marquage

► Aim to create an atmosphere of undercover detective work here!
Bemühe dich um eine Atmosphäre von geheimer Detektivarbeit!
Vise à créer une atmosphère de travail de détective secret !

Jazz

14. Clean Machine

Saubere Sache • Machine à nettoyer

► Aim for clean intervals with no spare notes in the gaps.
Bemühe dich um saubere Intervalle ohne überzählige Töne.
Vise à obtenir des intervalles propres sans « notes superflues » entre.

Jazz

15. Destination Waltz

Schicksals-Walzer • Destination Valse

► Keep this one moving along. Bars pass by very quickly in a jazz waltz so look well ahead.

Behalte in diesem Stück das Tempo bei. In einem Jazzwalzer gehen die Takte schnell vorbei, blicke deshalb weit voraus.

Conserve ceci en avançant. Les mesures évoluent très rapidement vers une valse de jazz, donc anticipe bien.

16. Mystery Man

Geheimnisvoller Mann • Homme mystérieux

► Try to spread the triplets evenly over the crotchet beat and don't arrive at the next note too early.

Versuche die Triolen gleichmäßig auf den Viertelpuls zu verteilen und spiele den nächsten Ton nicht zu früh.

Essaie de distribuer les triolets de manière régulière sur le temps de la noire et n'arrive pas trop tôt sur la note suivante.

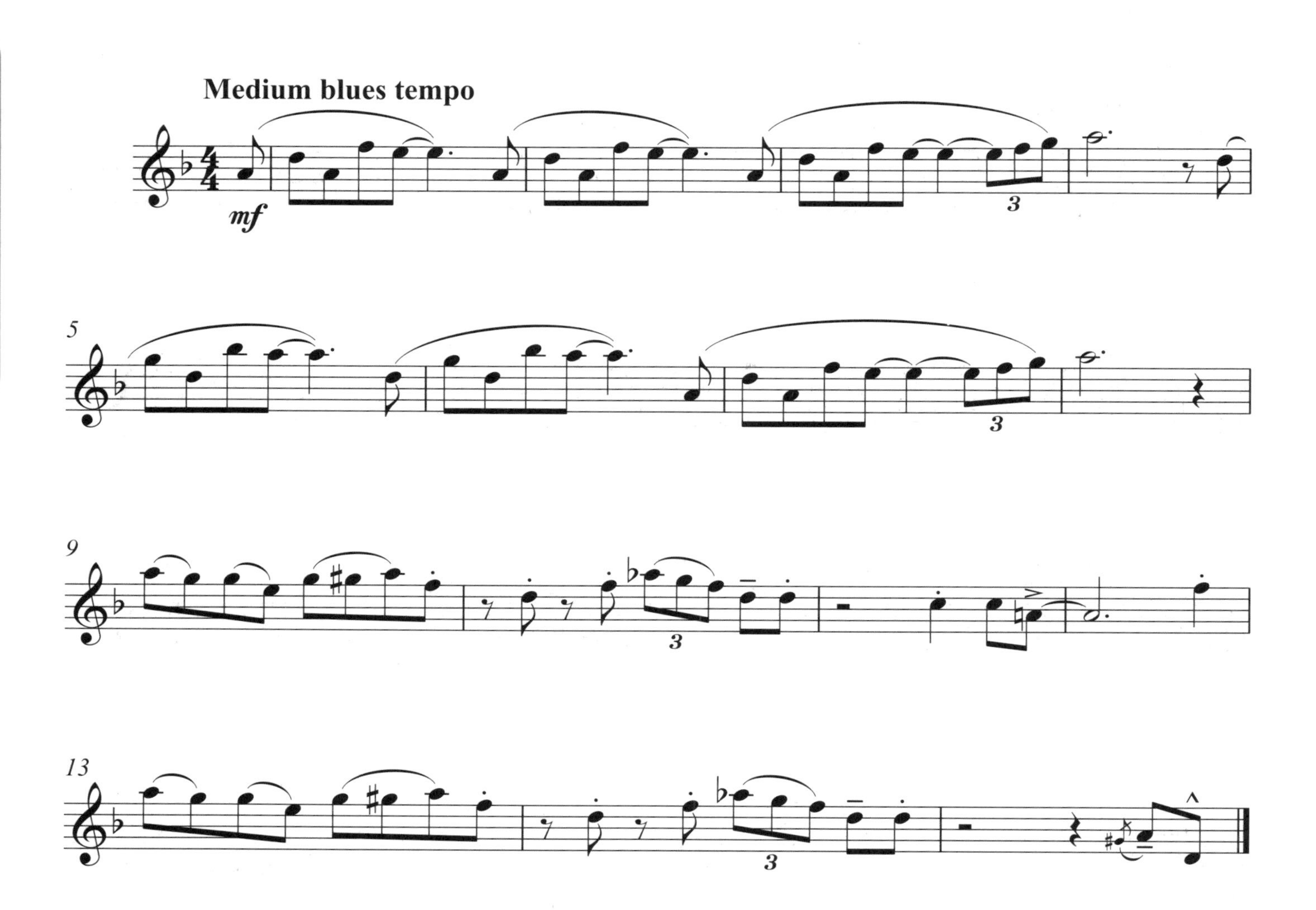

17. Doin' the Rounds

Runden drehen • En faisant des ronds

► Always aim to place the off-beat notes accurately before the bar lines.

Bemühe dich immer, die synkopierten Noten genau vor dem Taktstrich zu platzieren.

Essaie toujours de placer les notes à contretemps avec précision avant les barres de mesures.

18. Full On

Vollgas • Plein gaz !

► Play this piece with lots of drive and try not to lose speed on the quaver passages.

Spiele dieses Stück mit sehr viel Energie und versuche, bei den Achtel-Passagen nicht das Tempo zu verlieren.

Joue cette pièce avec beaucoup d'énergie et n'essaie pas de perdre de la vitesse sur les passages en croches.

Jazz

19. Street Moves

Straßentanz • Mouvements de rue

► Carefully observe all articulation in order to achieve a good stylistic performance.

Führe alle Artikulationszeichen sorgfältig aus, um eine stilistisch gute Interpretation zu erreichen.

Observe avec attention toute l'articulation de manière à accomplir une bonne exécution stylistique.

Jazz

20. High Five

► Make sure that this piece stays in 5 and do not be tempted to add a sixth beat!

Achte darauf, dass das Metrum bei fünf Zählzeiten pro Takt bleibt und füge keinen sechsten Schlag hinzu!

Assure-toi que cette pièce reste à 5 et ne sois pas tenté d'ajouter un sixième temps !

Rock

All quavers in this section of the book are to be played evenly.
Alle Achtelnoten in diesem Abschnitt des Buches sollen gleichmäßig gespielt werden.
Toutes les croches dans cette section du recueil doivent être jouées avec régularité.

21. The Time Has Come

Die Zeit ist reif • Le Temps est venu

► Always keep a steady pulse, especially in the rests.
Halte immer einen gleichmäßigen Puls, besonders in den Pausen.
Garde toujours une pulsation franche, spécialement dans les silences.

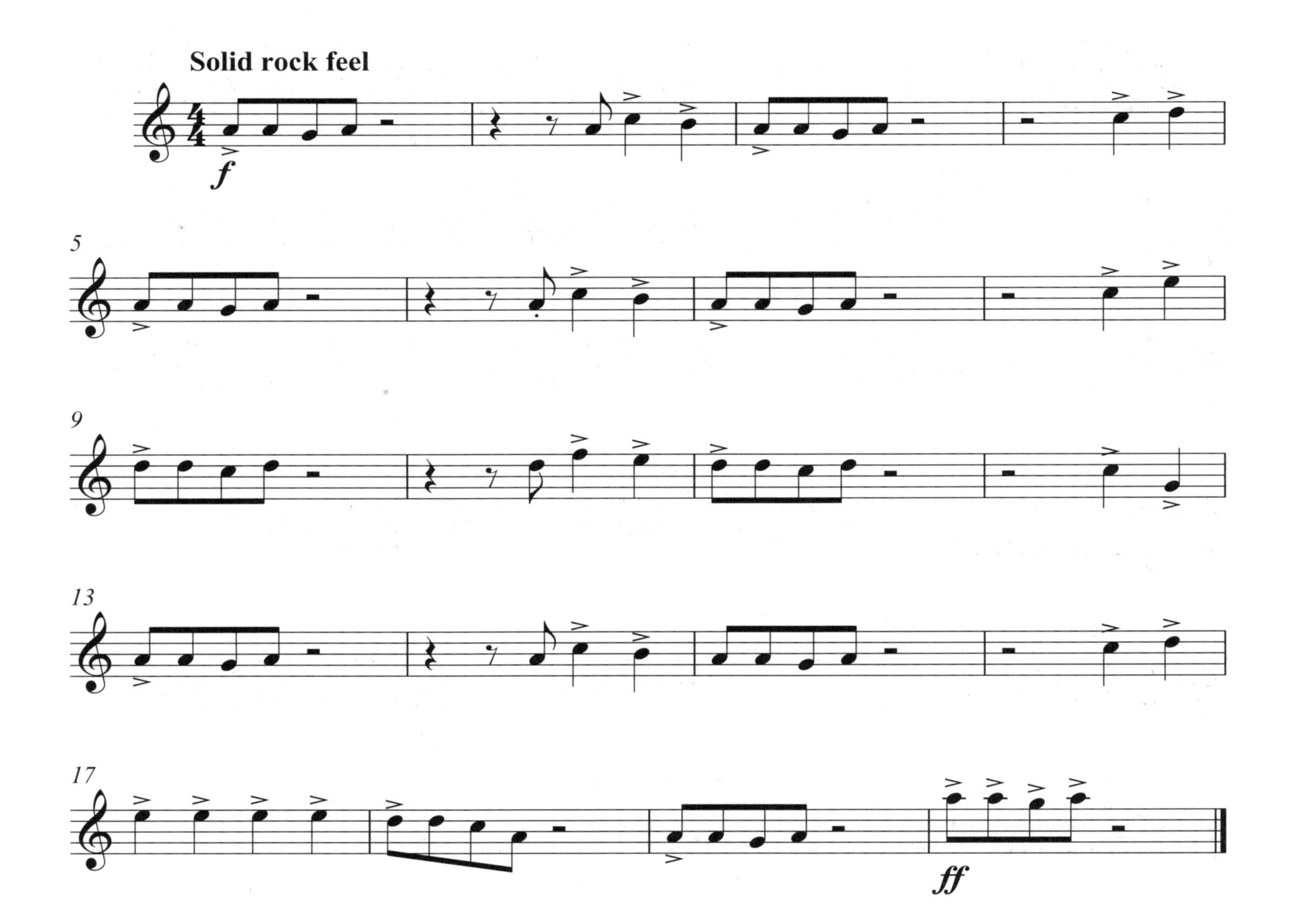

22. Bricks and Mortar

Ziegel und Mörtel • Briques et mortier

► Play this very positively and observe all markings carefully.

Spiele dieses Stück mit einer sehr positiven Einstellung und befolge die Vortragsanweisungen genau.

Joue ceci de manière très positive et observe attentivement toutes les marques.

Rock

23. Heavy Duty

Schwere Pflicht • Un lourd devoir

► Play this one with a great sense of purpose.
Spiele dieses Stück sehr entschlossen.
Joue ceci avec une grande détermination.

24. Hard Slog

Schinderei • Dure tâche

► Use a firm finger action here, especially on the A flats.
Setze hier kräftige Fingerbewegungen ein, besonders bei dem Ton „As".
Utilise ici une ferme action du doigt, spécialement sur les la bémol.

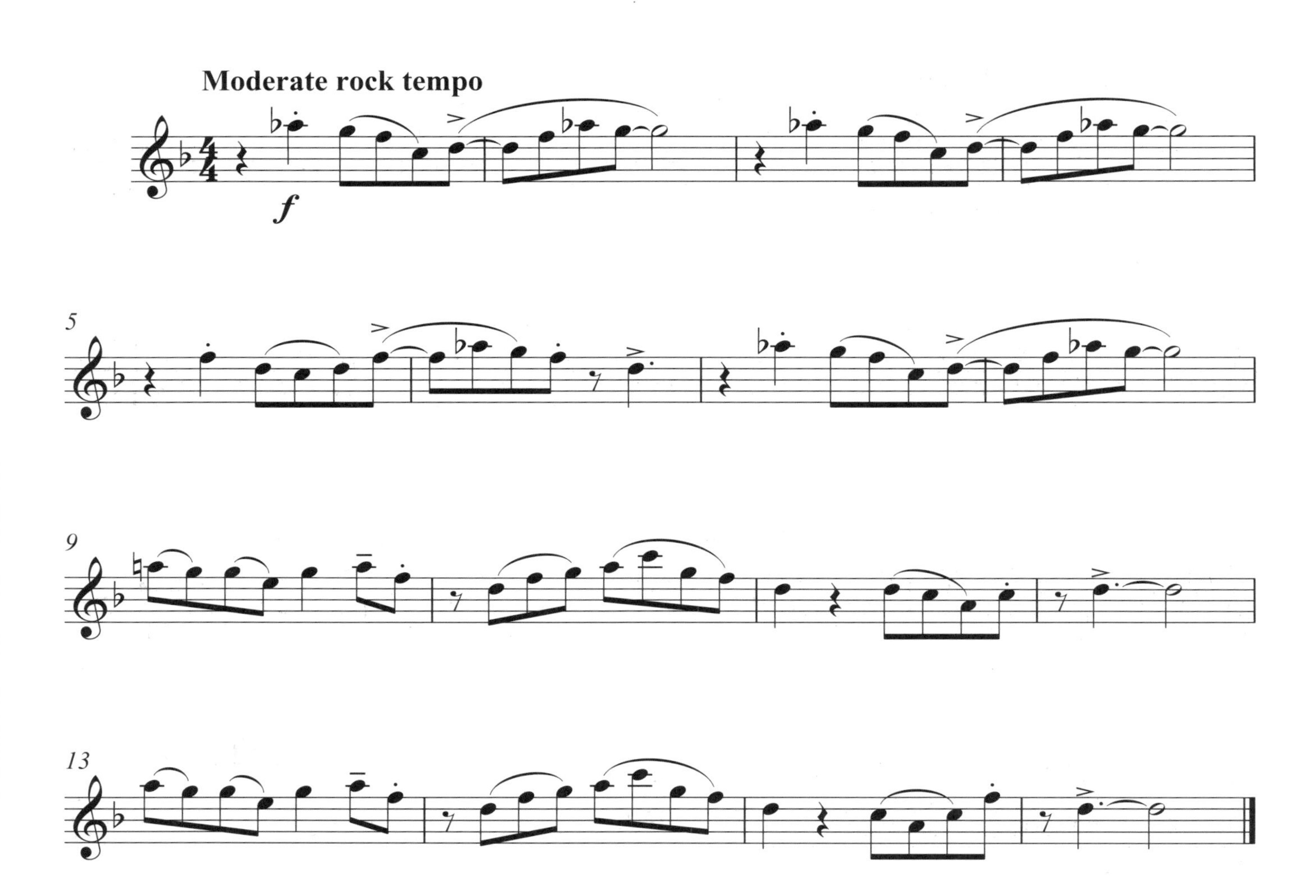

Rock

25. Sweet Sorrow

Süße Sorge • Douce peine

► Play this very expressively and give the long notes their full value.
Spiele dieses Stück sehr ausdrucksstark und halte den vollen Wert der langen Noten aus.
Joue ceci de manière très expressive et donne aux notes longues leur pleine durée.

Rock

26. Sax Un-Plugged

► No rules here, just go for it big time!

Keine Regeln, lege dich einfach voll ins Zeug!

Pas de règles ici, passe seulement un grand moment!

27. Headbanger

Harte Nuss • Bandeau

► Keep a steady pulse here and don't try to rush.
Halte einen gleichmäßigen Puls und versuche im Tempo nicht zu laufen.
Garde ici une pulsation ferme et n'essaie pas de presser.

Rock

28. Four by Four

Vierradantrieb • Quatre par quatre

► Play this piece with lots of punch and really bring out the accents.
Spiele dieses Stück mit viel Kraft und hebe die Akzente wirklich deutlich hervor.
Joue cette pièce avec beaucoup de punch et fais vraiment ressortir les accents.

29. Kickin'

Strampeln • Ruade

► Observe all articulation markings, especially the staccatos on the fourth semi-quavers.

Führe alle Artikulationszeichen sorgfältig aus, besonders die Staccati auf der vierten Sechzehntelnote.

Observe toutes les marques d'articulation, spécialement les staccatos sur les quatrièmes doubles croches.

Rock

30. Hot House

Treibhaus • Maison chaude

► Keep this one moving along and don't let your tongue slow you down.

Behalte in diesem Stück ein forsches Tempo bei und lasse nicht zu, dass deine Zunge das Tempo verlangsamt.

Garde ceci en avançant et ne laisse pas ta langue te retarder.

Rock

Latin

All quavers in this section of the book are to be played evenly.
Alle Achtelnoten in diesem Abschnitt des Buches sollen gleichmäßig gespielt werden.
Toutes les croches dans cette section du recueil doivent être jouées avec régularité.

31. Flying South

Flug in den Süden • Survolant le Sud

► Most of the phrases here start with a crotchet rest. Be careful not to come in too early.
Die meisten Phrasen beginnen hier mit einer Viertelpause. Pass auf, dass du nicht zu früh einsetzt.
Ici la plupart des phrases commencent par un soupir. Sois attentif de ne pas y arriver trop tôt.

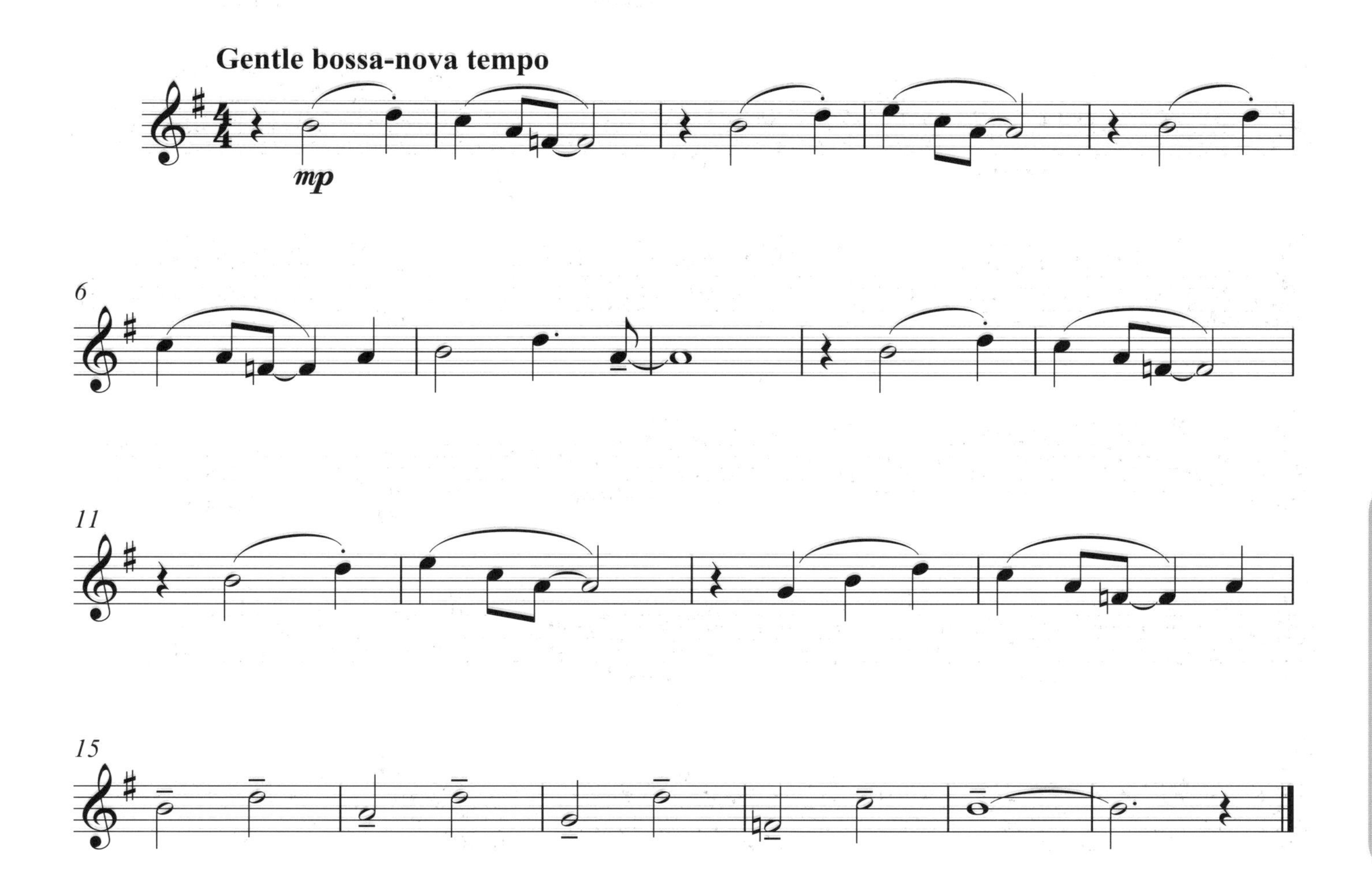

32. Warm Front

Warmfront • Front chaud

► Keep this one nice and light and don't be tempted to overblow.
Spiele dieses Stück gefällig und leicht und achte darauf, nicht zu überblasen.
Garde une conduite agréable et légère et ne sois pas tenté de t'enflammer.

Latin

33. Limbo!

► Try to keep a solid two in a bar feel throughout this piece and watch out for the ending!

Versuche in diesem Stück immer, die zwei schweren Zählzeiten hervorzuheben und achte auf das Ende!

Essaie de garder une solide sensation de mesure à deux tout au long de la pièce et fais attention à la fin !

Latin

34. Sierra Tango

► Spread the crotchet triplets evenly over the pulse and aim to sustain the long notes.

Verteile die Vierteltriolen gleichmäßig auf den Puls und bemühe dich, die langen Noten auszuhalten.

Distribue de manière égale les triolets de noires sur la pulsation et essaie de tenir les longues notes.

Latin

35. The Three Note Samba

► Play this piece with lots of energy and do not let it drag.
Spiele dieses Stück mit viel Energie und verschleppe nicht das Tempo.
Joue cette pièce avec beaucoup d'énergie et ne la laisse pas traîner.

Latin

36. Bossa Bossa

► Play this very gently with a relaxed feel and observe all articulation markings.

Spiele dieses Stück sanft und mit einem Gefühl der Entspannung. Beachte alle Vortragsanweisungen.

Joue ceci très doucement avec un sentiment de relâchement et observe toutes les marques d'articulation.

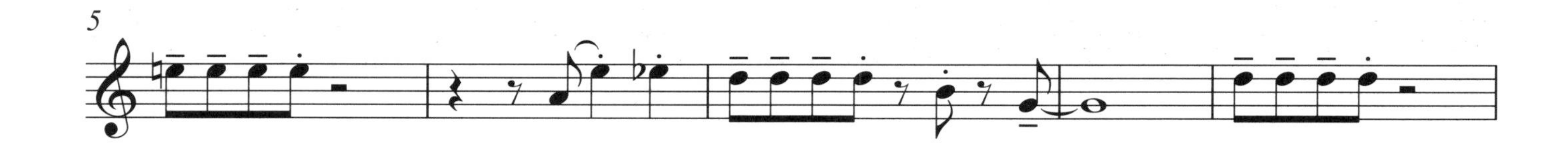

37. Sunset Cruising

Segeln bei Sonnenuntergang • Croisière du crépuscule

► Play this with a very relaxed feel and don't put too much weight on the tenutos.

Spiele dieses Stück mit einem Gefühl der Entspannung und hebe die ausgehaltenen Noten nicht zu stark hervor.

Joue ceci avec un grand sentiment de relâchement et ne mets pas trop de poids sur les tenutos.

Latin

38. Blue Cockatoo

Blauer Kakadu • Cacatoès bleu

► Aim to play this piece with a sense of *cool accuracy* and take great care over the off-beats.

Bemühe dich in diesem Stück um coole Genauigkeit *und achte auf die Synkopen.*

Essaie de jouer cette pièce avec un sens de fraîche précision et prends grand soin des contre-temps.

Latin

39. Sangria

► Play this piece with lots of drive and observe the block changes of dynamics.

Spiele dieses Stück mit viel Energie und beachte die blockförmigen Änderungen der Dynamik.

Joue cette pièce avec beaucoup d'énergie et observe les changements de blocs de nuances.

40. Mambo Nova

► Warning! This piece contains large intervals. Use a firm finger action to avoid catching spare notes.

Achtung! Dieses Stück enthält große Intervalle. Bewege die Finger sehr stark, damit du keine zusätzlichen Töne spielst.

Attention! Cette pièce contient de grands intervalles. Utilise une ferme action du doigt pour éviter d'accrocher des notes superflues.

Latin